SHIRE NATURAL HIS

C000195525

UMBELLIFERS
of the British Isles

SABINA G. KNEES

CONTENTS

Introduction 2
Biology of the umbellifers 6
Distribution and habitats 10
Poisonous species 21
Further reading 24

Cover: *Giant hogweed (Heracleum mantegazzianum) in flower. The umbels may reach 60 cm across.*

Series editor: Jim Flegg.

Printed in Great Britain by C. I. Thomas & Sons (Haverfordwest) Ltd, Press Buildings, Merlins Bridge, Haverfordwest, Dyfed.

Introduction

Umbellifers comprise a large family of mostly herbaceous plants and are usually identifiable as members of a coherent group by their general appearance. About seventy species can be found in the British Isles and about half of these have a widespread distribution, the remainder being local or rare. Most of the species are native or widely naturalised, while several occur sporadically either as established garden escapes or as opportunist short-lived casuals. Since there are so many species, with the majority having divided and umbellate heads of white flowers, umbellifers have a reputation among amateur naturalists of being impossible to distinguish from each other. But with a little patience and experience nearly all can easily be identified using such criteria as habitat and time of flowering. Primitive man soon learnt to distinguish the edible species from the poisonous ones.

CLASSIFICATION

The Umbelliferae (or Apiaceae) is a large family containing about three thousand species in four hundred genera. They are distributed throughout the world with a concentration in the north temperate regions. The family is usually placed in the order Umbellales alongside the dogwood family, Cornaceae, and the ivy family, Araliaceae. Indeed, many taxonomists believe that the umbellifers have no single character distinguishing them from the ivy and its relatives and that they should be combined in one family. The ivy family contains mostly woody members with fleshy fruits while umbellifers are usually herbaceous and have dry fruits. Both families, however, share a common basic chromosome number. Although several numbers have been reported, eleven is the commonest haploid chromosome count (that is the number of chromosomes in the pollen grains and the ovum before they become united).

The Umbelliferae is divided into three unequal subfamilies: Apioideae, Saniculoideae and Hydrocotyloideae. The familiar white-flowered umbellifers such as carrot (*Daucus carota*) and parsley (*Petroselinum segetum*) belong in the Apioideae, which is the largest subfamily, containing about 90 per cent of all the species. Features of this subfamily include: leaves without stipules and a tendency towards multiple divisions; flowers in compound umbels; ovaries with prominent stylopodia (the swollen bases of the two styles), a feature more or less confined to this family; and a basic chromosome number usually of eleven. Saniculoideae contains four genera; three of these (*Sanicula*, *Astrantia* and *Eryngium*) are represented in the British Isles and may not at first be associated with umbellifers. Wood sanicle (*Sanicula europaea*), astrantia (*Astrantia major*), sea holly (*Eryngium maritimum*) and field eryngo (*E. campestre*) have simpler leaves which are often undivided and without stipules; flowers in simple umbels or capitula (*Eryngium*) and ovaries with flattened discs; the commonest basic chromosome number of the subfamily is eight. The third subfamily, Hydrocotyloideae, has been placed in a separate family by some taxonomists, but it does share some characters with the Saniculoideae which are sufficient to warrant its retention in the Umbelliferae. The leaves are usually simple with stipules; flowers are in simple umbels or whorls; ovaries have flattened discs; and the commonest basic chromosome number is eight. This subfamily is represented in Britain by the genus *Hydrocotyle*, commonly known as the pennyworts, and again may not be immediately recognised as associated with the Umbelliferae.

At the generic level the problem of classification intensifies since there are so many common features, giving rise to a great deal of overlap in diagnostic characters. This is especially problematic in the Apioideae and many botanists have suggested that the characters normally used to distinguish groups of plants at the specific level are used in Umbelliferae for the delimitation of genera. Consequently, most of the genera are small and many contain only one species; they are then said to be monotypic.

The classification of umbellifers occurring in the British Isles is presented as a

CLASSIFICATION OF UMBELLIFERS: THE BRITISH SPECIES

Umbellifers belong to the order of Umbellales and are the family Umbelliferae, which contains 420 genera and 3100 species with a cosmopolitan but chiefly north temperate distribution. It is usually divided into three subfamilies:

1. HYDROCOTYLOIDEAE. Leaves often simple, usually with stipules. Flowers usually in simple umbels or whorls. Ovary with a more or less flat disc. Fruit with woody endocarp; vittae absent in ripe fruit. Carpophore absent. Commonest basic chromosome number, 8.
Genus: HYDROCOTYLE. 2 species — *H. vulgaris, H. moschata.*

2. SANICULOIDEAE. Leaves often simple or palmately lobed, without stipules. Flowers in simple umbels or capitula. Ovary with a more or less flat disc. Fruit with a membranous endocarp. Vittae present in ripe fruit. Carpophore absent. Commonest basic chromosome number, 8.
Genera: SANICULA. 1 species — *S. europaea;* ASTRANTIA. 1 species — *A. major;* ERYNGIUM. 2 species — *E. maritimum, E. campestre.*

3. APIOIDEAE. Leaves usually divided, without stipules. Flowers usually in compound umbels. Ovary with a prominent stylopodium. Fruit with membranous endocarp. Vittae present in mature fruit. Carpophore present. Commonest basic chromosome number, 11.
Genera: CHAEROPHYLLUM. 2 species — *C. temulentum, C. aureum;* ANTHRISCUS. 3 species — *A. sylvestris, A. caucalis, A. cerefolium;* SCANDIX. 2 species — *S. pecten-veneris, S. australis;* MYRRHIS. 1 species — *M. odorata;* CORIANDRUM. 1 species — *C. sativum;* SMYRNIUM. 2 species — *S. olusatrum, S. perfoliatum;* BUNIUM. 1 species — *B. bulbocastanum;* CONOPODIUM. 1 species — *C. majus;* PIMPINELLA. 2 species — *P. major, P. saxifraga;* AEGOPODIUM. 1 species — *A. podagraria;* SIUM. 1 species — *S. latifolium;* BERULA. 1 species — *B. erecta;* CRITHMUM. 1 species — *C. maritimum;* SESELI. 1 species — *S. libanotis;* OENANTHE. 7 species — *O. fistulosa, O. pimpinelloides, O. silaifolia, O. lachenalii, O. crocata, O. aquatica, O. fluviatilis;* AETHUSA. 1 species — *A. cynapium;* FOENICULUM. 1 species — *F. vulgare;* ANETHUM. 1 species — *A. graveolens;* SILAUM. 1 species — *S. silaus;* MEUM. 1 species — *M. athamanticum;* PHYSOSPERMUM. 1 species — *P. cornubiense;* CONIUM. 1 species — *C. maculatum;* BUPLEURUM. 6 species — *B. rotundifolium, B. subovatum, B. baldense, B. tenuissimum, B. falcatum, B. fruticosum;* TRINIA. 1 species — *T. glauca;* APIUM. 4 species — *A. graveolens, A. nodiflorum, A. repens, A. inundatum;* TRACHYSPERMUM. 1 species — *T. ammi;* PETROSELINUM. 2 species — *P. crispum, P. segetum;* SISON. 1 species — *S. amomum;* CICUTA. 1 species — *C. virosa;* AMMI. 2 species — *A. majus, A. visnaga;* FALCARIA. 1 species — *F. vulgaris;* CARUM. 2 species — *C. carvi, C. verticillatum;* SELINUM. 1 species — *S. carvifolium;* LIGUSTICUM. 1 species — *L. scoticum;* ANGELICA. 2 species — *A. sylvestris, A. archangelica;* LEVISTICUM. 1 species — *L. officinale;* PEUCEDANUM. 3 species — *P. palustre, P. officinale, P. ostruthium;* PASTINACA. 1 species — *P. sativa;* HERACLEUM. 2 species — *H. sphondylium, H. mantegazzianum;* TORDYLIUM. 1 species — *T. maximum;* TORILIS. 4 species — *T. nodosa, T. leptophylla, T. arvensis, T. japonica;* CAUCALIS. 1 species — *C. platycarpos;* TURGENIA. 1 species — *T. latifolia;* DAUCUS. 1 species — *D. carota.*

table including eighty species, not all of which may occur at any one time. Several are short-lived casuals which persist during a succession of mild winters or in favourable habitats. Others have been introduced, usually by human agency, and have persisted long enough to become well integrated into the native flora.

MORPHOLOGY

The leaves of umbellifers are arranged alternately along the stems or, in some biennial (flowering in the second year) and monocarpic (flowering once before dying) species, in false basal rosettes. In most species the leaves are petiolate (stalked) and the vast majority have divided leaf blades. However, the genera *Bupleurum* and *Hydrocotyle* are two notable exceptions, each having simple, undivided leaves. The division can be simple so that the leaflets are in opposite pairs along the midrib (pinnate) or more complex so that each division may be further subdivided along its lateral veins into further divisions, hence two-pinnate, three-pinnate and so on. The leaves of carrots are usually two- to three-pinnate. In a few species the leaves are ternately divided. This means that the divisions are divided into three more or less equal parts. Further divisions are described as two-ternate or three-ternate. The leaves of ground elder (*Aegopodium podagraria*) are usually ternate or two-ternate. The petiole or leaf stalk may be channelled or grooved and in some species it

3

1. *Variation in leaves. (Left) Those of wild carrot (Daucus carota) are two- to three-pinnate: each division is divided along its lateral veins into further subdivisions. (Right) The leaves of ground elder (Aegopodium podagraria) are two-ternate: each division contains three more or less equal parts.*

becomes grossly exaggerated, clasping the stem for part of its length before abruptly contracting into the first division of the blade. Sheathing petioles or leaf bases are common in *Angelica* and *Smyrnium*. In some species the fibrous remains of leaf bases may persist at the base of the plant and this can be a useful diagnostic character. Honewort (*Trinia glauca*) and moon carrot (*Seseli libanotis*) usually have such remains at the bases of their stems. Flowering stems may be grooved, furrowed or smooth, hairy or hairless and sometimes blotched with reddish purple markings. The inflorescence or umbel may be subtended by bracts. A stylised umbellate inflorescence is shown in figure 2, but it is important to

realise that not all the parts may be present in all species and their presence or absence is therefore of diagnostic value. The smaller clusters of flowers, sometimes called partial umbels, secondary umbels, umblets or umbellules, are borne on short stalks usually referred to as rays. Each umbellule may or may not be subtended by a further set of bracts, which because of their position are normally called bracteoles. At the highest level of division in the umbel, the pedicels each support a single flower.

Each individual flower contains a calyx of five sepals, sometimes reduced to teeth or absent altogether. The five petals are usually equal, though in some species the outer petals of an umbel or umbellule

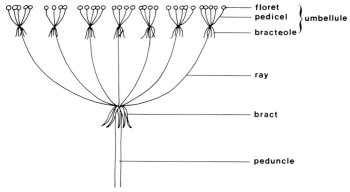

2. *Diagram of hypothetical umbel showing arrangement of bracts, rays and bracteoles and the composition of the umbellule.*

4

3 (left). *Sheathing leaf bases of petioles in alexanders (Smyrnium olusatrum).*

4 (centre). *Simple leaves in marsh pennywort (Hydrocotyle vulgaris).*

5 (right). *The only woody umbellifer likely to be found in Britain is the shrubby hare's-ear (Bupleurum fruticosum). The simple evergreen leaves and golden yellow flowers are very distinctive. Although a native of southern Europe, this well known ornamental garden plant is naturalised in several localities.*

may be much longer. Each petal may be hairy or smooth, notched at the apex and inflexed (bent upwards) or incurved (bent downwards). The five stamens alternate with the petals and surround the two-celled ovary, which in the subfamily Apioideae is topped by two styles and their enlarged bases or stylopodia. The fruit is usually composed of two dry one-seeded carpels, which may be compressed laterally, for example stone parsley (*Sison amomum*), or dorsally, for example hogweed (*Heracleum sphondylium*), and are joined by a central axile stalk or carpophore. The fruit splits at maturity and is thus a schizocarp, but since it always splits into two these are referred to as mericarps. Each mericarp may have five to nine ribs or ridges and these may be slightly raised or thin and wing-like, for instance hemlock (*Conium maculatum*). In some species a further set of ridges positioned between the main or primary ridges exists; these are usually called secondary ridges because of their relative position. They may, however, exceed the primary ridges in size. Sometimes there is additional ornamentation between the ridges in the form of small projections or papillae, for example the hare's-ears (*Bupleurum* species), or in the form of spines or hooks, for example the hedge-parsleys (*Torilis* species) and the sea holly. Four resin canals, or vittae, usually lie between the primary ridges, although they are not always obvious, and two further vittae sometimes occur on the inner connecting face of each mericarp, usually known as the commisural surface. The fruits in some species have long beaks of tissue above the seed-bearing part, for example the shepherd's needle (*Scandix pecten-veneris*), while in others the calyx becomes thickened and persists as a crown of teeth, for example the dropworts (*Oenanthe* species) and cowbane (*Cicuta virosa*).

IDENTIFICATION

The most important features to examine when attempting to identify umbellifers are the shape and degree of dissection of the leaves; the presence or absence of bracts and bracteoles; the number and length of the rays; and a number of characters associated with the fruits. Individual flowers tend to be relatively similar, often varying only in minute detail from species to species; however, they do display some useful differences which can aid identification at

5

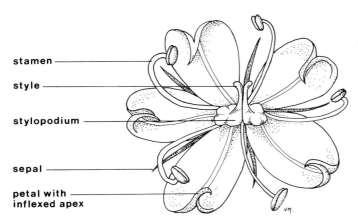

stamen

style

stylopodium

sepal

petal with
inflexed apex

the generic level. Flower colour is one of the most obvious characters and, although the majority are white, umbellifers with yellow, pink, green and blue flowers all occur in the British Isles. There are very few species growing in Britain with a unique set of characters. The sea holly is the only native blue-flowered species, while the shrubby hare's-ear (*Bupleurum fruticosum*) is the only woody species likely to be found. Although not native in the British Isles, it is often grown as a garden plant and has become naturalised in Devon, Kent and Worcestershire.

Biology of the umbellifers

POLLINATION

Unlike many groups of flowering plants, the Umbelliferae has a relatively high degree of floral uniformity. This may represent an interesting adaptation from an evolutionary point of view, encouraging free pollination by a wide range of unspecialised pollinators. The effects of what is often termed pro-miscuous pollination are twofold: the species can increase its natural distribution without the need to attract specific pollinators, but only at the cost of what is

usually considered to be an effective isolating mechanism. Within such para-meters it is almost inappropriate to dis-cuss breeding systems since nearly all species are self-fertile and hybridisation is rare. However, a closer look at the umbellifers in a locality will reveal subtle differences within the apparently uniform flower heads of the different species. The floral features commonly shared by umbellifers in the largest subfamily, Apioideae, are a prominent stylopodium, exposed nectar, promiscuous pollination, perfect flowers (that is having functional stamens, styles and ovaries) with the exception of honewort (*Trinia glauca*), protandrous flowers (where the stamens mature before the ovary) and sexual reproduction. The stylopodia are often large and brightly coloured (for example in the carrot) and this may be a secondary device to attract additional pollinators. The majority probably visit to feed on the copious quantities of nectar provided by the plants; the nectar must be prolonged to continue to attract pollinators when the stigmas become receptive, which may be some time after the anthers have ripened. Some biologists suggest that nectar may be produced in sequence by a series of flowers within the umbel.

As previously mentioned, the outer petals of flowers occurring at the peripheral rim of the compound umbel are sometimes much larger than those elsewhere in the flower head. These are described as radiate petals and are found

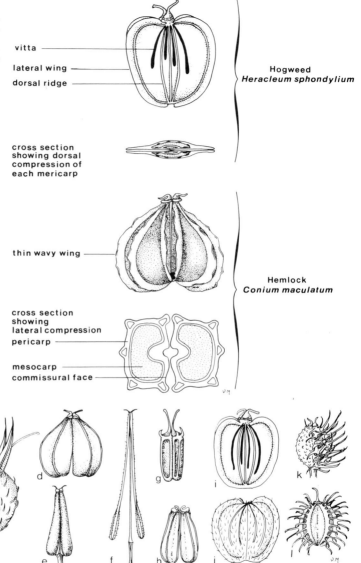

7. *Fruit types in the Umbelliferae. Note the comparison between the dorsally compressed hogweed (Heracleum sphondylium) and the laterally compressed hemlock (Conium maculatum).*

vitta

lateral wing

dorsal ridge

Hogweed
Heracleum sphondylium

cross section showing dorsal compression of each mericarp

thin wavy wing

Hemlock
Conium maculatum

cross section showing lateral compression

pericarp

mesocarp

commissural face

8. *Selection of fruit types: a, marsh pennywort (Hydrocotyle vulgaris); b, sanicle (Sanicula europaea); c, sea holly (Eryngium maritimum); d, alexanders (Smyrnium olusatrum); e, cow parsley (Anthriscus sylvestris); f, shepherd's needle (Scandix pecten-veneris); g, corky-fruited water-dropwort (Oenanthe pimpinelloides); h, thorow-wax (Bupleurum rotundifolium); i, wild parsnip (Pastinaca sativa); j, hartwort (Tordylium maximum); k, knotted hedge-parsley (Torilis nodosa); l, wild carrot (Daucus carota). Note: the persistent sepals in sea holly (Eryngium maritimum) and corky-fruited water-dropwort (Oenanthe pimpinelloides); the slender stalk or carpophore in shepherd's needle (Scandix pecten-veneris); tubercles in marsh pennywort (Hydrocotyle vulgaris); hooks and spines on sea holly, sanicle (Sanicula europaea), knotted hedge-parsley (Torilis nodosa) and wild carrot (Daucus carota); and vittae in wild parsnip (Pastinaca sativa). (Not to scale.)*

9 (left). *Wild carrot (Daucus carota), showing central purple decoy floret.*

10 (right). *Rock samphire (Crithmum maritimum), flowering in August on a rocky coastline. Note the fleshy, bluish green foliage which contrasts well with the greenish yellow flowers.*

in the hogweeds and carrot. The effect is similar to that found in the daisy (*Bellis perennis*) and many other members of the Compositae, where the flower head is composed of numerous groups of small flowers. The outer ring of the daisy flower consists of white ray florets, while the yellow centre is a group of tiny disc florets; however, the overall effect is of a single flower. This clever deception attracts insects which might not normally be drawn to the compound inflorescence which is typical of umbellifers and composites. Insect visitors to umbels may spend some time sitting on or walking over the inflorescence, inadvertently col-

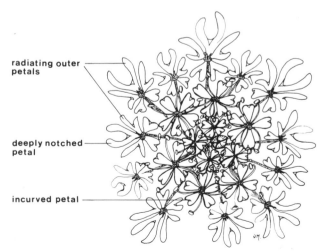

radiating outer petals

deeply notched petal

incurved petal

11. *Umbellule of hogweed (Heracleum sphondylium), viewed from above. Note the radiating outer petals.*

12 (left). *Sea holly (Eryngium maritimum), showing the bluish green, leathery, spine-tipped leaves and bracts, and the blue flowers in dome-shaped, thistle-like heads.*

13 (right). *Honewort (Trinia glauca), a local species with male and female flowers growing on separate plants. Its distribution is restricted to limestone near the coast.*

lecting pollen, which is redistributed to other flowers. Between two and three hundred different pollinating species have been recorded but the commonest are the Diptera (flies, gnats, mosquitoes). Some of the smaller Coleoptera (beetles) do visit umbellifers but, as many of the plants contain unpalatable oils, these chewing and sucking insects are often deterred. The umbels of some species of *Daucus*, including the common carrot, often have a central blackish purple flower which acts as a decoy, perhaps ensuring the visit of otherwise

14 (left). *Alexanders (Smyrnium olusatrum), a stout glossy-leaved perennial which flowers in early spring.*

15 (centre). *(Angelica sylvestris), one of the most widespread species, occurs throughout the British Isles, often in damp habitats.*

16 (right). *Field eryngo (Eryngium campestre) is a very local species confined to dry grassland in southern England.*

uninterested pollinators.

Shorter styles and reduced stylopodia occur in many flowers of the lateral and terminal umbels in a compound inflorescence. These flowers are functionally male, whilst the remainder are hermaphrodite (that is they have all reproductive parts present and functional). Male and hermaphrodite flowers occur in varying proportions throughout the family but their significance is poorly understood. One hypothesis suggests that the hermaphrodite flowers supply an extra pollen reservoir, ensuring the successful pollination of the earliest flowers, and this may explain why there are often more male flowers in secondary and tertiary (later-flowering) umbels.

DISPERSAL

Despite the apparent uniformity of the fruit, several adaptations for effective dispersal have successfully evolved within the family. The most obvious are the hooked spines on the fruits of *Daucus* and *Torilis* species. These enable the fruits to be dispersed by any animal with sufficient hair to trap them. The persistent spiny calyx teeth on the fruits of sea holly and field eryngo (*Eryngium campestre*) perform a similar function. Fruits of *Angelica* and *Heracleum* species have broad lateral wings that are thin and papery, enabling effective wind dispersal. Some of the aquatics such as the dropworts (*Oenanthe* species) and rock samphire (*Crithmum maritimum*), a coastal umbellifer, have thick corky outer seed coats (pericarps) which enable the fruits to float until a site suitable for eventual germination is reached.

Distribution and habitats

ECOLOGY

Ecological studies are concerned with biological economics, that is the investigation of interactions and relationships between any one species and its immediate environment. The varying combination of available light and water, soil type, geology and temperature in association with seasonal change determines the development of distinct habitats. Umbellifers are particularly successful from an ecological standpoint, occurring in a wide range of habitats, though in Britain they are rarely found in moorland or mountainous regions. They are well adapted to thrive in areas modified by human activity. Umbellifers are not generally tolerant of deep shade and more commonly occur in open habitats. Another example of their ecological success is shown by the ability of non-native species to integrate or become established, perhaps at the expense of native species. Ground elder was probably introduced during the Roman occupation of Britain and is now one of the most prevalent species, absent from only a few localities in the Pennines and the higher mountains of Scotland and Wales.

Although some species may be found in a range of habitats, others are more specific. It is sometimes possible to identify specimens by eliminating certain species which would not normally be present in some particular vegetation type. For example, the lesser water-parsnip (*Berula erecta*) would not be found in chalk grassland because it is restricted to freshwater ditches, pond margins and similar riverine situations. The following sections summarise the major habitats where umbellifers grow, describing in more detail some of the species which may easily be confused.

COASTAL SPECIES

The rock samphire (*Crithmum maritimum*) is perhaps the only British umbellifer which could be described as an obligate halophyte: one that has become adapted to live in an environment with higher than average salt levels. Specimens grown away from the damp salty conditions on coastal cliffs, rocks, shingle or sand dunes rarely survive for more than one or two seasons. Other characteristics distinguishing this species include greyish green succulent leaves which are two or three times pinnately divided, each lobe terminating in a short hard spine. When crushed, these leaves produce a strong, slightly sweet odour. In former times these were often pickled. The umbels are produced from late June to early September on stalks of 15 to 45 cm and vary in diameter, having between eight and 35 rays and striking yellowish green flowers. The fruits are rhombic in cross-section, with thick prominent longitudinal ridges. The mesocarp is spongy, becoming corky as the fruit matures, enabling it to float. Rock samphire is commonly seen in the coastal habitats of southern and western England, Wales, southern Scotland and Ireland. It is absent from the colder coasts of eastern England and Scotland.

The sea holly (*Eryngium maritimum*) is also confined to coasts but prefers sand dunes. It is occasionally found on shingle but rarely if ever on cliffs or rocky shores. So many characters separate this species from all other British umbellifers that a detailed description is not necessary. The thick leathery leaves are greyish blue and spine-tipped with undulating margins, very like those of the holly (*Ilex aquifolium*) — hence its common name. The flowers are also unique in their bluish white colour, arranged into compact and elongated thistle-like heads. The flowering plant may vary from 15 to 60 cm in height, depending on its situation, and normally flowers in July and August. The fruits are also very distinctive, with long protuberances covering most of the surface and persistent sepals forming a spiny crown.

Scots lovage (*Ligusticum scoticum*) is also restricted to the coastal extremities but in this species the limitations seem to be climatic rather than geological. It is found only on the rocky coasts of Scotland and the northern part of Ireland, with just one locality on the westernmost point of Galway in the Republic of Ireland. Scots lovage is a striking plant with bright red petioles, contrasting well with the glossy, bright green leaf blades, which are twice ternately divided. The individual lobes are oval in outline and have saw-like teeth crowded towards the apex. This combination of colours is also often reflected in the flowers, which are greenish white and sometimes have a pinkish tinge. These fine umbels are

carried on stems of 20 to 90 cm in June and July. Historical records show that the leaves were once used as a pot herb and their subtle flavour may also explain why Scots lovage does not persist in areas where sheep graze regularly.

The remaining species associated with coasts are extremely local and are not likely to be encountered by chance. The hog's fennel or sulphur weed (*Peucedanum officinale*) is an impressive yellow-flowered umbellifer with flowering stems of 1 or 2 metres arising from a stout woody base which is crowded with the fibrous remains of old leaf bases. The leaves are three to six times ternately divided into long narrow lobes with translucent cartilaginous margins. This species is now confined to about four localities in Kent and Essex, where it occurs on cliffs and banks.

The small hare's-ear (*Bupleurum baldense*) is one of the few annual umbellifers, sharing with the previous species yellow flowers and an apparent need for close proximity to the sea. It rarely exceeds 10 cm in height and, like several other species in the genus, has simple leaves and conspicuous bracts which surround and exceed the umbels. The small hare's-ear occurs in short turf and other very open habitats like rocky ground or semi-stabilised dune slacks, where there is little competition from other plants.

The only other species exclusively associated with maritime habitats is the honewort (*Trinia glauca*). The one remarkable feature about this plant is the occurrence of male and female flowers on separate plants; species exhibiting this unusual phenomenon are described as dioecious. This species is also very local, being confined to dry limestone grassland above the Avon Gorge and similar habitats in the vicinity and to one locality in south Devon.

BRACKISH HABITATS

Several umbellifers favour habitats where the water in river estuaries or in habitats inland contains salt levels above average, though they will grow elsewhere. The wild celery (*Apium graveolens*) often occurs as a garden escape in several parts of Britain but is considered native along river margins and

17 (above). *Cow parsley (Anthriscus sylvestris), the commonest white-flowered umbellifer, adorns roadsides throughout the British Isles in early spring.*

18 (below left). *Hogweed (Heracleum sphondylium), a rather coarse species, is unmistakable with its large hairy leaves and flat, white-, pink- or greenish-flowered umbels, from late May to early August.*

19 (below centre). *Sickle-leaved hare's-ear (Bupleurum falcatum) is one of the largest species in an unusual group of yellow-flowered umbellifers with simple leaves.*

20 (below right). *Lesser water-parsnip (Berula erecta) is commonly found in damp ditches and shallow water in lowland Britain, but is rare in Wales and Scotland.*

21 (above). *Sweet Cicely (Myrrhis odorata) flowers at about the same time as cow parsley, but only in northern Britain.*

22 (below left). *Moon carrot (Seseli libanotis), a very local species occurring in chalk grassland, is distinguished by the dense accumulation of fibres around the base of the stem, and the hairy fruits and pedicels.*

23 (below centre). *Ammi visnaga, a close relative of the bullwort, also occurs as a casual alien but is distinguished by its more finely divided leaves and rays which thicken in fruit.*

24 (below right). *Bullwort (Ammi majus) is a stout annual, often reaching 1 metre or more, with conspicuous leafy bracts and large untidy umbels of white flowers. It is frequently found in rubbish tips, occasionally appearing in gardens from bird-seed mixtures.*

other areas with brackish water near the sea. It is more frequent in southern and eastern England but occurs locally in similar habitats in Wales, north-eastern England, southern Scotland and sporadically around the Irish coast. The stems of this species are deeply grooved and reach about 1 metre when fully mature. The whole plant emits a strong smell of celery and it is this characteristic, combined with the lack of bracts, bracteoles and sepals, and the simply pinnate, often yellowish leaves, which distinguishes this species from other white-flowered umbellifers.

The parsley water-dropwort (*Oenanthe lachenalii*) is the only species in the genus which is commonly found in brackish water, although it does also occur in suitable freshwater habitats. The lower leaves are from one- to three-pinnate, and have rounded or oval-shaped lobes with a parsley-like appearance, which are probably responsible for its common name. These soon wither and the upper leaves which remain are one- or two-pinnate with narrow linear lobes 2 to 5 cm long. The stems are solid and may reach 1 metre when mature. The flowers are white and borne in umbels of five to nine rays with a concentration of male flowers around the perimeter of each umbellule. These male flowers are even more conspicuous since they have longer pedicels raising them above the remaining flowers in the centre. This species has a long flowering period from June through to September.

Also associated with brackish or coastal habitats but in a looser sense are alexanders (*Smyrnium olusatrum*) and the bur chervil (*Anthriscus caucalis*). These two species are easily distinguished by a number of characters. The bur chervil is a well branched slender annual of 25 to 80 cm, with hollow stems which often have a rich purple colouring at the base. The leaves are two to three times pinnately divided and hairy beneath. The umbels have only three to six rays, each about 1 cm long, and four to five bracteoles. The white flowers are borne in May and June and are followed by very distinctive fruits, which are shortly beaked and covered in hooked spines. Alexanders is a much stouter individual

and normally biennial. The solid flowering stems reach 50 to 150 cm and have two to three times ternate or pinnate glossy, yellowish green leaves. The rays are 3 to 4 cm long and range from seven to fifteen per umbel. These are topped by rich yellowish cream flowers unlike any other umbellifer in flower from April to June. The fruits are rounded, with three prominent ridges, and eventually turn brownish black. Both species occur in scattered localities around the coasts of Britain but are absent from the extreme north-west.

FRESHWATER HABITATS

Since a number of species are associated with watery or damp habitats it is useful to isolate the few which can be considered as obligate aquatics from those which grow equally well in marginal situations. One feature shared by all of the species in freshwater habitats is the presence of hollow stems, presumably an adaptation to their aquatic lifestyle in assisting buoyancy with these air-filled chambers. The river water-dropwort (*Oenanthe fluviatilis*), greater water-parsnip (*Sium latifolium*), lesser marshwort (*Apium inundatum*), lesser water-parsnip (*Berula erecta*) and fool's water-cress (*A. nodiflorum*) all spend most of their life cycle in water. All have white flowers in the summer but can be distinguished by a number of characters. The lesser water-parsnip and fool's watercress both have simply pinnate leaves and in favourable situations may reach about 1 metre in height. They can be separated by the presence of four to seven three-partite or pinnatifid bracts, and leaves with five to nine pairs of lobes in the lesser water-parsnip, with two to four pairs of lobes and no bracts in fool's watercress. The remaining three species have two types of leaves: the submerged, which are two or three times pinnately divided and often short-lived, and the aerial, which tend to be persistent and vary in their degree of dissection. The most distinct is the greater water-parsnip, which usually attains 2 metres and has simply pinnate aerial leaves with three to six pairs of lobes. The umbels have bracts and bracteoles and twenty to thirty rays. This species is not very common, occur-

14

ring only in a few isolated localities in Ireland and south-east England. The lesser marshwort and river water-dropwort both spend most of their time submerged, the river water-dropwort being more commonly found in flowing than still waters. Both species are fairly local, but the lesser marshwort is more widespread. The river water-dropwort has five to ten rays and mature fruits 5 to 6.5 mm long, with a crown of persistent sepals. The lesser marshwort has only two rays (rarely up to four), no sepals and smaller fruits, only 2.5 to 3 mm long.

The cowbane (*Cicuta virosa*) and the fine-leaved water-dropwort (*Oenanthe aquatica*) both tend to occur on the margins of ponds and ditches which are subject to seasonal dryness. The cowbane is described in detail in the section on poisonous species. The fine-leaved water-dropwort is an erect annual or biennial, varying in height from 30 to 150 cm, having tuberous roots when young. These are often close to the surface and easy to see but degenerate as the plant comes into flower. The leaves are of two types: the submerged have filiform segments, while the upper are triangular in outline and two to three times pinnately divided. The white umbels are 2 to 4 cm in diameter and usually have between four and sixteen rays. The mature fruit is 3.5 to 4.5 mm long.

The genus *Oenanthe* contains seven native species, making it the largest genus of the Umbelliferae in the British Isles. *O. fistulosa*, the tubular water-dropwort, is another species occurring in shallow water or in very wet meadows. This erect perennial has large tubular roots and slender hollow stems which are constricted at the nodes, giving a balloon-like appearance to the stems. The umbels have only two to four rays and are topped with white or often pink-tinged flowers. The fruits are 3 to 4 mm long and have very conspicuous teeth.

Although normally found in damp meadows, the whorled caraway (*Carum verticillatum*) also occurs in shallow water on the margins of ponds and lakes and in streams and gulleys. It is not a common species, being confined to acid substrates in the extreme west of England, Scotland and Wales and in similar areas in south-

west Ireland. These habitats are usually mountainous regions where a high rainfall predominates. The long narrow basal leaves are simply pinnate, with up to twenty pairs of deeply divided lobes. At first glance these leaves are very reminiscent of the common yarrow (*Achillea millefolium*) but the presence of fibrous leaf remains around the base distinguishes the whorled caraway. The flowers are white and the umbels have between eight and fourteen rays.

Also occurring in marginal situations are the hemlock water-dropwort (*Oenanthe crocata*), wild angelica (*Angelica sylvestris*), hemlock (*Conium maculatum*) and giant hogweed (*Heracleum mantegazzianum*). Three of these are discussed in the section on poisonous umbellifers but angelica is harmless and frequently occurs along river margins, in ditches, open woodland and damp meadows. It is one of the most widespread species in the British Isles, absent only from steep mountain slopes. The stems may reach 2 metres and are dark reddish purple. The leaves are broadly triangular in outline and two to three times pinnately divided with toothed oval lobes. Normally flowering in July and August, the umbels have four to eleven rays and white or dusky pink flowers. Its close relative, the garden angelica (*A. archangelica*), is very similar in appearance but has green stems and greenish white flowers in May and June. Although widespread in northern Europe and Greenland, it is not native in Britain but has become naturalised in a few localities in central and eastern England. Angelica is perhaps best known for its stems and petioles, which are candied with sugar and used in confectionery.

GRASSLANDS

This category is not a natural ecological division but merely a convenient heading to include all species not discussed elsewhere. The different types of grassland are classified first as wet or dry and then on the basis of substrate (chalk, limestone, acid or peaty soils, clay and so on).

Many of the species mentioned in the section on freshwater habitats also occur in damp meadows and fens. Species not already mentioned include the marsh

25. *Marsh pennywort (Hydrocotyle vulgaris), a low creeping plant common in damp meadows and ditches.*

pennywort (*Hydrocotyle vulgaris*), milk-parsley (*Peucedanum palustre*), Cambridge milk-parsley (*Selinum carvifolium*), pepper saxifrage (*Silaum silaus*) and two species of water-dropwort, *Oenanthe silaifolia* and *O. pimpinelloides*.

The marsh pennywort, with its round leaves and creeping stems, commonly occurs in damp grassland, fens and ditches. The fens of East Anglia contain several umbellifers of interest and rarity, including the Cambridge milk-parsley, which is restricted to just three localities although it is quite widespread in continental Europe. It is a perennial with solid stems reaching about 1 metre when flowering. The leaves are two to three times pinnately divided, each lobe being ovate in outline. The umbels have 15 to 25 unequal rays and spreading bracteoles, and white flowers from July to October, followed by narrowly winged, dorsally flattened fruits 3 to 4 mm long.

Also occurring in East Anglia, but not exclusively, is the milk-parsley. Although found in fens and similar situations to the Cambridge milk-parsley, it can be distinguished easily by its hollow purplish stems, deflexed bracteoles and fruits 4 to 5 mm long. This species is also well known to naturalists as the food plant of the swallow-tail butterfly and its larvae.

The two remaining species of water-dropwort are both restricted to damp meadows in southern England. They are tuberous-rooted perennials, but in the corky-fruited water-dropwort (*Oenanthe pimpinelloides*) the tubers are some distance from the base of the stem, whilst in the narrow-leaved water-dropwort, they occur almost immediately at the junction with the stem. The flowering stems of both species reach about 1 metre and have white flowers. The leaves are from one- to four-pinnate with long linear lobes in the narrow-leaved water-dropwort and only one- or two-pinnate with toothed ovate lobes in the corky-fruited water-dropwort.

With the exception of the marsh pennywort, the pepper saxifrage is the commonest species in the grassland group. This perennial has solid stems to about 1 metre characterised by the longitudinal grooves and fibrous remains of leaf stalks around the base. The leaves are one to four times pinnately divided, dark glossy green with red-tipped apices. The umbels have four to fifteen rays and unusual creamish yellow flowers. In addition, the stylopodium is often bright red. The pepper saxifrage is one of the many umbellifers in flower in meadows and on grassy banks from June to August.

Of the species occurring in dry grassland and similar open habitats, those having a specific requirement for chalk are relatively few and serve as good indicator species for this very specialised type of substrate. Wild parsnip (*Pastinaca sativa*), moon carrot (*Seseli libanotis*) and

16

greater pignut (*Bunium bulbocastanum*) are all reliable indicators of chalk near the surface, but the last two are extremely local in distribution. They grow in close association with other species confined to this specialised habitat in open grassland along the Chiltern range. Moon carrot is one of the rarest umbellifers in England, being restricted to areas of ancient turf on chalk and apparently dependent on continuous grazing for its existence as it is easily swamped by other species once grazing ceases. The solid stems are surrounded by the fibrous remains of old leaf bases and the leaves are narrowly triangular in outline and two- to three-pinnate, the individual lobes being ovate or lance-shaped and deeply toothed along their margins. The flowers are white and have conspicuous sepals and usually bloom in July and August. The fruit is 2.5 to 3 mm long and covered in soft hairs. Greater pignut is a slender perennial with stems varying between 30 and 100 cm tall, arising from a rounded dark brown tuber some distance below the surface. The stem gets narrower and is white below ground. The leaves tend to be confined to the base of the stem and are broadly triangular in outline, two-pinnate with long narrow lobes. The umbels have ten to twenty rays, five to ten bracts and bracteoles and white flowers in June and July. The fruit is 3.5 to 4.5 mm long and has conspicuous reddish brown vittae.

Wild parsnip is quite common on chalky substrates and is a familiar roadside plant in southern England. It has angled stems up to 1.8 metres tall and simply pinnate leaves with eight to eleven pairs of lobes. The strong parsnip smell and bright yellow flowers distinguish this species from other British umbellifers.

The only species which is specific to limestone grassland is honewort, already described in the section on coastal umbellifers. Similarly, only one species is a regular indicator of acid soils. Pignut (*Conopodium majus*) is very rarely found on chalky soils and so is unlikely to be confused with its close relative, the greater pignut. The plants are similar in overall appearance but the pignut is usually smaller, the stems rarely exceeding 60 cm and the umbels having only six to twelve rays. Also, its flowering period

from May to June is somewhat earlier.

Two species are specific to mountain pastures. The masterwort (*Peucedanum ostruthium*) is a stout hollow-stemmed perennial reaching about 1 metre, with large ternately divided leaves and heads with thirty to sixty unequal rays. The flowers are white and the fruits almost round and dorsally compressed, having prominent lateral wings. This species is not native to the British Isles but has become naturalised along river banks and in grassy places in hilly country in northern England and Scotland. Baldmoney (*Meum athamanticum*) is native to Britain and has a similar distribution but also occurs in North Wales. This species has fine delicate foliage, smelling strongly of aniseed. The hollow stems rarely exceed 60 cm and are surrounded by the fibrous remains of old leaf stalks. The lower leaves are three- to four-pinnate and the umbels have six to fifteen unequal rays, three to eight bracteoles, white flowers and disproportionately large fruits, up to 7 mm long. Both species are widespread in mountainous regions of Europe.

Other species occurring in grassy places include field eryngo (*Eryngium campestre*), burnet-saxifrage (*Pimpinella saxifraga*), corn parsley (*Petroselinum segetum*), stone parsley (*Sison amomum*) and longleaf (*Falcaria vulgaris*). Longleaf is not native to Britain but has become naturalised in south-east England. It is unique in having leaves which are three times divided into long lobes with saw-like teeth. These divisions are sometimes further divided and described as two- or three-fid. The umbels have long bracts and bracteoles and creamish white flowers from July to September. The field eryngo is a close relative of the sea holly and has very spiny leathery leaves and greenish white thistle-like flower heads. It is very local, being confined to a few areas in southern England and Wales. The remaining three species all have simply pinnate leaves and are fairly slender perennials growing to about 1 metre, with white-flowered umbels. Stone parsley is strong-smelling and has leaves with two to five pairs of leaflets and umbels with three to ten unequal rays, while the burnet-saxifrage has two different types of leaves. The lower are simply pinnate with four to six pairs of toothed oval lobes and the upper are two-pinnate with linear lobes. The umbels have ten to twenty rays and white flowers which are very occasionally tinged pink.

CULTIVATED LAND

The number of umbellifers occurring specifically in arable land has diminished during the twentieth century, largely due to an increase in the use of herbicides and more intensive agricultural practice. The annuals which once frequented cereal fields are now as rare as poppies and cornflowers and like them occur only on newly disturbed ground, being unable to compete amongst the perennial species normally found in permanent grassland. The rarest are described by Tutin (1980) and include thorow-wax (*Bupleurum rotundifolium*), small bur-parsley (*Caucalis platycarpos*) and the great bur-parsley (*Turgenia latifolia*); all are species from Mediterranean Europe.

Four species occurring more readily in arable land are shepherd's needle (*Scandix pecten-veneris*), fool's parsley (*Aethusa cynapium*), spreading hedge-parsley (*Torilis arvensis*) and knotted hedge-parsley (*T. nodosa*). Fool's parsley is the largest and by far the commonest of the four species, with stems often exceeding 1 metre and frequently reaching 120 cm. Its most distinguishing features are the three or four long beard-like bracteoles occurring on each outer, white-flowered umbellule. The leaves are triangular or lance-shaped in outline and two- to three-pinnate. This species is very poisonous, containing similar polyacetylenes to those found in hemlock. The three remaining species are shorter, rarely exceeding 50 cm, and may be easily distinguished by their fruits.

Shepherd's needle has umbels with only one to three rays, white flowers and fruits 30 to 70 mm long in which the majority of the length is the beak, the part which is not the seed-bearing portion. The two hedge-parsleys have white or pink flowers and one- to two-pinnate leaves. The knotted hedge-parsley has almost stalkless umbels with two to three rays borne in the leaf axils, which look like small burs when the plant is fruiting. The individual fruits are also remarkable

because each mericarp in a pair of outer flowers is different: one has long hooked spines while the other is covered in tubercles. In contrast, the spreading hedge-parsley has umbels of three to five rays on long peduncles and fruits with hooked spines on both mericarps. The fruits of the inner flowers of each umbel all have spineless mericarps. These dimorphic fruits represent an interesting ecological adaptation as the outer fruits of each umbel serve to disperse the species away from the parent plant and are easily detached from the carpophore, whereas the inner fruits are spineless and remain until the plant rots — hence maintaining the local population. The closely related *Torilis leptophylla* very rarely occurs as a casual and differs in its longer rays.

Another species occurring in cultivated land, more specifically damp lawns, is the New Zealand marsh pennywort (*Hydrocotyle moschata*). It differs from the British native in its smaller, toothed leaves on petioles only up to 5 cm, whilst those of *H. vulgaris* are usually between 10 and 25 cm long. Also, it is quite strongly aromatic. Pignut is another frequent umbellifer of damp, slightly acidic lawns. Two further species associated with cultivated land, particularly in urban areas, are aliens which have grown from bird-seed mixes. Neither are particularly common: the false thorow-wax (*Bupleurum subovatum*) is an annual with entire leaves which surround the stem at their bases. The flowers are small and yellow and the whole plant rarely exceeds 30 cm. The other species, *Trachyspermum ammi*, does not have a common name, probably because it is so rarely seen in Britain. It is a white-flowered annual ranging between 10 and 30 cm, with densely tuberculate fruits and two- to three-pinnate leaves with linear lobes.

A few species formerly cultivated for flavouring have become established in odd localities throughout Britain. They are not widespread and are rarely encountered but still deserve to be included. Garden chervil (*Anthriscus cerefolium*) was formerly naturalised in Herefordshire and may occur in a few other localities. It is similar to the bur chervil but has much larger fruits (7-10 mm

18

long). Lovage (*Levisticum officinale*) is a stout perennial up to 2 metres tall with greenish yellow flowers. Dill (*Anethum graveolens*) is a slender annual which sometimes occurs as a garden escape. It has foliage and flowers reminiscent of fennel (*Foeniculum vulgare*). *Smyrnium perfoliatum* and *Astrantia major* are two European species cultivated for their ornamental value and often become established in suitable localities. All species are described in greater detail in Tutin (1980).

WASTE GROUND

Most of the species which occur in these very transient habitats are aliens from Europe and beyond and include several umbellifers of interest. Ground elder and hemlock are often found in localities where nitrogen levels are higher than average, and rubbish tips often contain nitrogenous waste. Other nitrophilous species are cow parsley, garden angelica and fool's parsley. *Trachyspermum ammi*, false thorow-wax, *Ammi* species and coriander (*Coriandrum sativum*) are also common casual species often found on waste ground. Coriander is easily recognised by its strong-smelling foliage and rounded fruits. It is a slender annual, rarely exceeding 50 cm, with rounded three-fid lower leaves, finely divided upper leaves and purplish white flowers. Two species of *Ammi* are frequent casuals in Britain. Both are annuals with solid stems. *A. majus* often reaches heights of 1 metre or more and has very variable deep bluish green leaves, the lower one- or two-pinnate with oval or lance-shaped lobes and deeply toothed margins, the upper finely divided with entire margins. The umbels are rather untidy with nine to forty rays, long conspicuous bracts which are often leaf-like, and white flowers. *A. visnaga* is a smaller species, rarely exceeding 60 cm, with finely divided yellow-green foliage and similar bracts. The rays become thickened and stiff after flowering. *Scandix australis*, a close relative of the shepherd's needle, is sometimes found in rubbish tips or on waste ground. It differs in having a more compressed beak on the fruit, so that the seed-bearing part is not clearly differentiated, as it is in *S. pecten-*veneris.

ROADSIDES AND HEDGEROWS

Here, a succession of umbellifer species can be seen throughout the year and in all parts of Britain. Cow parsley, keck or Queen Anne's lace (*Anthriscus sylvestris*) is usually the first to appear, its bright green leaves coming into active growth at the end of February in the milder counties. This is the commonest of the early-flowering species, its creamy white flowers dominating roadsides from April to June. The leaves are three-pinnate with toothed lobes and the stems are hollow, ranging from 60 to 150 cm. The umbels have six to twelve rays, four to six conspicuous bracteoles and oblong fruits 6 to 9 mm long. In northern England and Scotland sweet Cicely (*Myrrhis odorata*) is also in flower at this time of the year. However, this plant differs in having white markings on the leaf and a strong aniseed fragrance when crushed. The fruits are much larger (15 to 25 mm), with sharp ridges, and are a glossy dark brown when fully mature.

Next to appear is the rather coarse hogweed (*Heracleum sphondylium*), which is equally common throughout Britain. The bulky one- to two-pinnate leaves are dark green and have rough hairs over both surfaces. The sheathing petioles can be confused only with the giant hogweed (see 'Poisonous species'). The flowers are white, pink or greenish and have deeply notched radiate petals on the edge of each umbellule. The vittae are obvious on the mature fruits, which are almost round and 7 to 9 mm long. Whilst this species is still flowering, the rough chervil (*Chaerophyllum temulentum*) appears. It may at first be confused with cow parsley but differs in its roughly hairy stems, which are often swollen below the nodes, and purple or purplish spotting towards the base. Rough chervil usually flowers from May to July and is further characterised by the number of rays in its umbels (only six to twelve), which are often nodding in bud. Slightly later-flowering but otherwise similar is the golden chervil (*C. aureum*), an alien species naturalised in southern Scotland and southern England. It is larger, often reaching 1.5 metres, with

19

26 (left). *Astrantia (Astrantia major), a common species of mountain grassland in southern Europe, is naturalised in several localities in Britain, especially in the north and west.*

27 (centre). *Hemlock water-dropwort (Oenanthe crocata) in one of its favoured habitats, the damp shallow margins of a lake, flowering in June. This plant is poisonous.*

28 (right). *Giant hogweed (Heracleum mantegazzianum) growing as an ornamental plant in the Valley Gardens, Windsor Great Park. The 3 metre flowering stems are ideal in large wild gardens.*

pale yellowish green leaves that are broadly triangular in outline, and umbels with 12 to 25 rays. Also flowering in June and July and sometimes naturalised along roadsides are hartwort (*Tordylium maximum*) and caraway (*Carum carvi*). Although a native of Asia and North Africa, caraway occurs throughout Europe, probably because it is widely cultivated for its fruits, which are used for flavouring. It is biennial with hollow stems 30 to 60 cm tall and white, pink or reddish flowers in umbels of five to sixteen unequal rays. Although widely distributed in Britain, it is not common. Hartwort is very restricted in its distribution, occurring in just a few localities in south-east England. It is a very distinctive species with rough hairy stems up to 130 cm, simple basal leaves and simply pinnate upper leaves. The five to fifteen rays are covered in bristles and the flowers of the outer umbellules are radiate. The fruits are dorsally compressed with a thickened whitish ring around the perimeter. Another alien which has become well established is fennel (*Foeniculum vulgare*). This species is very distinct with its greyish green three- to four-pinnate leaves with thread-like lobes, and golden yellow flowers from July to October. It is more common in southern Britain, especially around the coasts. The greater burnet-saxifrage (*Pimpinella major*) is another species of roadsides and hedgerows with a distribution concentrated in eastern Britain. The stout stems are 120 cm tall and the leaves are glossy green and simply pinnate with three to four pairs of lobes. The umbels lack bracts and bracteoles and have ten to twenty rays and white or pink flowers. Once found along the roadsides of Essex but now possibly extinct is the sickle-leaved hare's-ear (*Bupleurum falcatum*), a woody-based perennial with simple lance-shaped leaves and small yellow flowers blooming from July to October. This species is doubtfully native and may reappear in the future.

One of the latest-flowering umbellifers common on roadside verges and hedgebanks is the upright hedge-parsley (*Torilis japonica*). This attractive annual has bristly grey-green stems up to 120 cm and one- to three-pinnate leaves. The six to ten rays are rather unequal and the flowers are pinkish or purplish white, blooming from July to September, when chervil and hogweed are beginning to fade. As with other species in this genus, the fruits are covered with forward-pointing spines but in this species they are sometimes slightly curved, though not hooked. However, the most reliable difference is the presence of more than one bract (commonly four or five) in the upright hedge-parsley.

WOODLANDS

Few umbellifers occur only in woodland since many which may be found here also grow on river banks, roadsides and hedgerows. Wood sanicle (*Sanicula europaea*) and bladderseed (*Physospermum cornubiense*) are the only two species found exclusively in woodlands. Sanicle is quite common and in beech woods in southern England it is often the dominant herb species, particularly on sites where shallow soils and steep banks prevail. Sanicle also occurs in oak woodland but, since competition from other species is often greater, it is rarely dominant. Its shiny dark green leaves are palmately lobed and persist long after the plant has finished flowering. The umbels have just three rays and white flowers which are usually deep reddish pink in bud and are borne from May to August. The fruits are only 3 mm long but are distinguished by a covering of hooked bristles.

Bladderseed is doubtfully native in Britain, having a very curious distribution, with one site in Buckinghamshire and two or three in the oak woods of Devon and Cornwall. If it is truly native, these localities probably represent the northernmost limit of the species, which is quite widespread in the woodlands of southern central Europe. The flowering stems are long and slender, ranging from 30 to 120 cm. The leaves are two-ternate and the umbels have ten to fourteen rays, triangular sepals, four to seven bracts, white flowers and broad inflated fruits about 3 to 4 mm long, presumably responsible for the common name of the plant.

Angelica, hogweed, pignut, cow parsley and rough chervil are also commonly found in more open woodland, frequently on woodland margins.

Poisonous species

Man has had to learn which plants are poisonous and which are safe to eat. By definition, any plant adversely affecting the health of man or his domestic animals can be considered poisonous. However, the degree of toxicity may vary according to the health of the individual and the quantity of the plant ingested. Also, for many plants which contain high levels of toxic substances, the part which is eaten and the stage of maturity of the plant may greatly affect the result.

Although the majority of umbellifers growing in the British Isles are harmless, a few have been suspected as the cause of poisoning and four species can cause severe poisoning, especially in livestock. These are cowbane (*Cicuta virosa*), hemlock (*Conium maculatum*), hemlock water-dropwort (*Oenanthe crocata*) and fool's parsley (*Aethusa cynapium*). Veterinary Investigation Diagnosis Analysis records over the two-year period of 1975 to 1977 show that 10 per cent of all cases of reported plant poisoning in animals involved the first three species. There are also cases of fatal human poisoning, particularly from the hemlock water-dropwort, which has been eaten in mistake for celery, parsley and watercress.

Unlike hemlock and hemlock water-dropwort, cowbane is not common in Britain. Its restricted distribution is a reflection of the exacting habitat requirements of the species. It is confined to ditches, marshes or areas of permanent shallow water. With marked changes in land use during the twentieth century, many of the localities where cowbane would normally be found have been drained or otherwise destroyed, making this one of the many species experiencing a decline. Cowbane is one of the more distinctive white-flowered umbellifers, forming stout perennial plants with ridged, hollow stems reaching 30 to 150 cm. The roots are characterised by having hollow chambers, which are easily seen in longitudinal section. The leaves are broadly triangular in outline, pinnately divided with long narrow segments, each with regularly toothed margins. The leaf surface is dull and colours well in autumn, from rich reddish brown to pale greenish yellow; carefully planted, cowbane makes an attractive garden plant. However, the siting is very important since plants which are highly poisonous should not be grown in places readily accessible to children or livestock. The flowers are borne in dense umbels, 7 to 13 cm across, subtended by leafy bracts. The rays vary from ten to thirty per head. Cowbane normally flowers in July or August. The rather bitter, unpleasant smell of all its parts should be sufficient to deter anyone from trying to eat it.

The poisonous principle is cicutoxin, an unstable higher alcohol which is concentrated in the yellow sap of the roots. The toxin reaches its highest levels of concentration during late autumn and early winter, once the leaves have died down but before the plant is fully dormant. The accidental ingestion of part of one root has been responsible for the death of horses, cattle and even children. Remarkably, the poison does not degrade much even after drying. Cowbane roots which have been dug and left lying on banks after ditch clearing are quite attractive to curious livestock and may still cause death several months after they have been uprooted and are apparently dead.

Hemlock is probably one of the most widespread of British umbellifers and appears to be increasing its distribution (see figure 30). It is commonly seen as the dominant plant along new motorway or trunk road cuttings, especially if there is a watercourse nearby. These quite attractive, tall slender plants often exceed 2 metres. The foliage is finely divided and the green stems are smooth and marked throughout their length with irregular purplish blotches. At the time of flowering, late May to early July, the basal leaves usually start to yellow. They are drooping or withered by the time fruits have developed on the umbels. Each fruit is well rounded with wing-like frills on the dorsal and lateral ridges. The plant is characterised by its 'mousy' or musty smell, especially noticeable when the stems or leaves are bruised. It can be recognised instantly by the large number of umbels, which seem to be too small for the size of the plant.

Hemlock was thought to be unique among umbellifers, plant biochemists in the 1970s describing it as the only species in the family producing alkaloids. However, further research has shown the chemical to be a polyacetylene, coniine. Hemlock is said to have been the poison the Greek philosopher Socrates was required to take as a suicide draught.

Also known as dead men's fingers because of the five or more fleshy finger-like tubers, hemlock water-dropwort has a scattered distribution in Britain. The plant may be locally abundant along watercourses or in the margins of lakes and ponds. Oenanthe crocata usually forms an erect perennial varying from 50 to 150 cm high, with deeply grooved hollow stems. The leaves are slightly shiny and divided into pinnately compound leaflets, each more or less oval in outline with unevenly toothed margins. The white flowers are borne on twelve to forty rays in hemispherical to spherical umbels 5 to 10 cm across, from late May to early July. All parts are quite strong-smelling. The tubers are creamish white and exude a clear sap which yellows on exposure to the air.

The poisonous principle in hemlock water-dropwort is oenanthetoxin, biochemically classified as a poly-unsaturated higher alcohol. The toxin is concentrated in the roots but all parts of the plant would prove poisonous if ingested. Since this species is a herbaceous perennial which by definition dies down in the winter, the toxins become highly concentrated in the tuberous roots when the plant is dormant. Fatal cases of poisoning from this species have occurred in humans when the leaves have been mistaken for celery or parsley and the roots as parsnip.

Several species of umbellifer have been isolated as the specific cause of contact dermatitis in susceptible individuals. Since skin reaction to plant chemicals has been proven to be dependent on light levels, the condition is often referred to as photodermatitis. The worst cases occur when sensitive individuals come into contact with the sap of the plant in the presence of strong sunlight. The most commonly cited examples are from celery, parsnip, parsley, angelica, carrot, hemlock and giant hogweed.

Probably the most spectacular of all umbellifers is the giant hogweed (*Heracleum mantegazzianum*). Its towering stems cannot be confused with any other species and since its introduction as a garden ornamental from the Caucasus in 1895 it has spread considerably. It had already found its way into the British Isles before this deliberate introduction, however, and contemporary records indicate knowledge of the plant in scattered localities throughout Britain from 1817. Its rapid spread along watercourses and through other suitable habitats would not give cause for concern were it not for the problems encountered by the many people sensitive to its toxic sap.

The plants are biennial or short-lived perennials, forming large basal rosettes up to 150 cm high and 2 to 3 metres across. Flowering stems produced in the second or third year vary from 3 to 5.5 metres tall, are deeply grooved, coarsely hairy and usually a rich reddish purple at the base, becoming spotted towards the top. The umbels have between 50 and 150 rays up to 30 cm long. The flowers are pure white with notched radiate petals around the outer rim of the umbel. Bracts and bracteoles are numerous and the fruits are 9 to 11 mm long with solitary vittae.

Several umbellifers can have a marked effect on milk if they are eaten by dairy cattle. These effects vary from tainting the milk with an unpleasant taste or smell to more serious contamination which changes the chemical composition of the milk to such a degree that it is no longer suitable for making butter, cheese or yoghurt. The most dramatic effects include a temporary drop in yield or even a total cessation of milk production. However, these cases are extremely rare and it is unlikely that humans would be

29 (above). *Hemlock (Conium maculatum), with blotched stems, many small-headed umbels and finely divided fern-like foliage.*

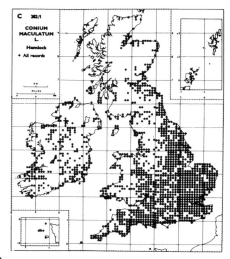

30 (right). *The distribution of hemlock (Conium maculatum) in the British Isles. It is one of the most widespread species, absent only from higher ground in the north and west.*

23

poisoned as a result of drinking contaminated milk.

The species responsible for causing a reduction in milk yield are cowbane and hemlock. Hemlock has also been isolated as one of the species which can taint milk, the other being fool's parsley.

Further reading

As there are so many umbellifers growing in the British Isles, some have been discussed only briefly here. For keys and more detailed accounts of all species, the Botanical Society of the British Isles handbook (by Tutin, 1980) is strongly recommended.

Clapham, A. R.; Tutin, T. G.; and Moore, D. M. *Flora of the British Isles*. Cambridge University Press, third edition 1987.

Cooper, M. R., and Johnson, A. W. *Poisonous Plants in Britain and Their Effects on Animals and Man*. Reference Book 161, Ministry of Agriculture, Fisheries and Food, Her Majesty's Stationery Office, 1984.

Godwin, H. *History of the British Flora*. Cambridge University Press, second edition 1975.

Heywood, V. H. (editor). 'The Biology and Chemistry of the Umbelliferae', *Botanical Journal of the Linnean Society*, 64, supplement 1. Academic Press, 1971.

James, T. J. 'Pignuts and Cow Parsley: Getting to Know Umbellifers', *Country-side Journal of the British Naturalists' Association*, 26 (2) (1988), 4-5, 30.

Keble-Martin, W. *The New Concise British Flora*. Michael Joseph, 1982.

Mitchell, J., and Rook, A. *Botanical Dermatology*. Greengrass Limited, Vancouver, 1979.

North, P. *Poisonous Plants and Fungi*. Blandford Press, 1967.

Perring, F. H., and Walters, S. M. *Atlas of the British Flora*. Ebury Press for the Botanical Society of the British Isles, second edition, 1976.

Phillips, R. *Wild Flowers of Britain*. Pan, 1977.

Ross-Craig, S. 'Umbelliferae', *Drawings of British Plants*, Parts XII to XIII. G. Bell and Sons Limited, 1958 and 1959.

Tampion, J. *Dangerous Plants*. David and Charles, 1977.

Tansley, A. G. *Britain's Green Mantle*. George Allen and Unwin Limited. second edition 1968.

Tutin, T. G. *Umbellifers of the British Isles*. BSBI Handbook 2, Botanical Society of the British Isles, 1980.

Tutin, T. G.; Heywood, V. H.; Burges, N. A.; Moore, D. M.; Valentine, D. H.; Walters, S. M.; and Webb, D. A. (editors). *Flora Europaea*, volume 2. Cambridge University Press, 1968.

ACKNOWLEDGEMENTS

The author wishes to thank Victoria Matthews for her care and attention to detail over the line drawings (figures 1, 2, 6, 7, 8, 11, 25) and Andrew McRobb for photographing the distribution map and drawing of hemlock (figures 20, 30). Figure 29 is reproduced from *Piosonous Plants in Britain and Their Effects on Animals and Man*, by M. R. Cooper and A. W. Johnson (HMSO, 1984), by permission of the Controller of Her Majesty's Stationery Office. Figure 30 is reproduced by permission of the Botanical Society of the British Isles. Other illustrations are acknowledged as follows: Martin F. Gardner, figures 3-5, 10, 12, 14-19, 21-4, 26-8; Dr Stephen L. Jury, figure 13; Sabina G. Knees, figures 9, 20, and the cover. Thanks are also due to Dr Stephen L. Jury, Jennifer Lammond and Mervyn Southam for technical advice.